• PETER PATILLA •

At Home with
Maths 1

• Oxford University Press •

2 + 5 - 8 + 4 + 10

Notes to parents

How to use this book:

- This activity book has been designed for children aged 5-6, to help support their work in the first year of school.

- It is intended to be fun to work through, so that the child goes off to school feeling that they enjoy mathematics.

- Though most of the tasks can be done unaided by the child, you may want to help with reading the instructions, discussing how to do the task, and filling in the results.

- The book is deliberately self-contained, requiring a minimum of further equipment.

- But it should be treated as a springboard to further investigations off the page, using all the mathematical opportunities that exist in the world around the child.

How to help your child:

- Don't expect your child to do too much at once; they can pick single pages that appeal to them, and work in short, keen bursts of activity.

- Help your child by discussing the activities, how to do them and the results; there may be more than one right answer, so let your child talk about the alternatives.

- If your child has difficulty with an activity, don't make them anxious about it; check whether they have a recurrent problem with a particular skill, or let them just move onto another activity.

- Give plenty of praise and encouragement.

What is the National Curriculum?

- The National Curriculum offers a framework of content and skills in different subjects for children aged 5-16.

- This series is designed for the 2 years of Key Stage 1, ages 5-7.

- Each subject is divided into Attainment Targets, which define the knowledge, skills and understanding in that subject; the grid on page 64 shows how the activities in this book relate to the Attainment Targets in mathematics.

- Children progress through different Levels of achievement, and these books cover the Levels appropriate to Key Stage 1.

What will my child get out of this book?

- Children should enjoy filling in each page of this book, and making it their own record of achievement.

- There is a 'traffic light' in the bottom corner of each page for self-assessment: your child can fill in 1 if they enjoyed the activity a little, and up to 3 points if they enjoyed the activity a lot. This will indicate to you their particular strengths, likes and dislikes.

Contents

Sorting all sorts of things

Colour the animals with tails.

Colour all the things which can fly.

Sorting opposites

Draw hats on the happy faces.
Which are the sad faces?

Which bottles are full?
Colour in the empty bottles.

Sorting for size

Find the small octopuses. Colour them yellow.
Find the large octopuses. Colour them red.

Find the medium-sized crocodiles.
Colour them green.

Making more

Here are some flowers.
Draw one more flower.

Here are some wiggly worms.
Draw one more wiggly worm.

Finding the odd one out

Ring the odd one out.

Making something different

Make one picture different from the other.

Matching things which are the same

Join pairs which are the same.

Make each pair the same.

Counting objects

Join each child to a toy.
Are there any toys left over?

Join bowls to spoons.
Are any spoons missing?

Each elephant eats one bun.
How many buns are left over?

Making sets have the same number

Make these strings have the same number of beads.

Make each pair of ladybirds have the
same number of spots.

Making one set have more than another

Draw pips in each pair of oranges.
Make one orange have more pips than the other.

11

Finding the most

Colour the card in each set with the highest number.

Finding the least

Colour the card in each set with the lowest number.

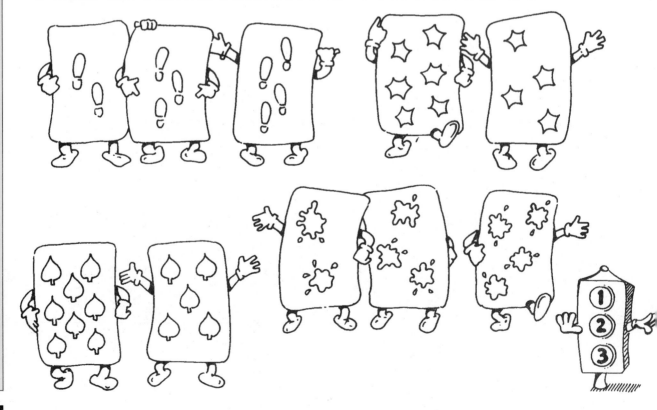

Estimating numbers

Look at the sweets in each jar.
Do you think there are more coloured sweets or white sweets?
Tick below each jar.
Then count to check if you are right.

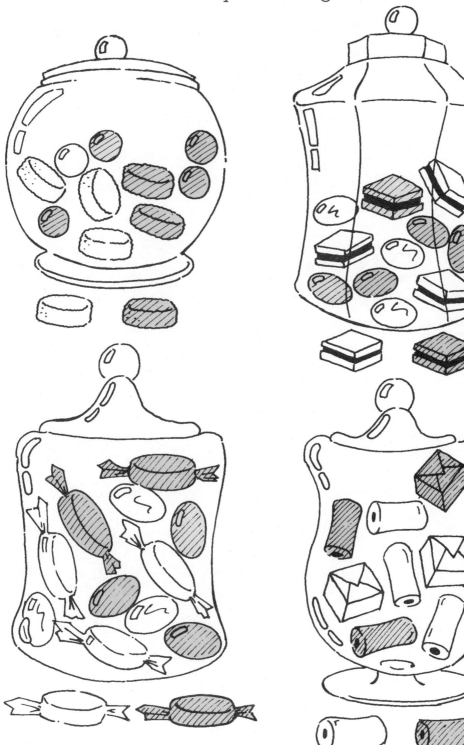

Practising writing numbers 0-4

0 0 0 0 0 0 0 0 0 0 0 0

1 1 1 1 1 1 1 1 1 1 1 1

2 2 2 2 2 2 2 2 2 2 2

3 3 3 3 3 3 3 3 3 3 3

4 4 4 4 4 4 4 4 4 4

Practising writing numbers 5-9

5   5 5 5 5 5 5 5 5 5 5 5

6   6 6 6 6 6 6 6 6 6 6 6

7   7 7 7 7 7 7 7 7 7 7 7

8   8 8 8 8 8 8 8 8 8 8 8

9   9 9 9 9 9 9 9 9 9 9

15

Seeing numbers all around you

Where might you see numbers which look like these?
Join the numbers to the pictures.

2:30

e
450g
contents

Z
ED

H37 WVO

38 Windmoor
via Crook Estate

BUS

JS4JOM

①
②
③

Finding numbers on things we use

Write in the missing numbers.

Counting objects

How many birds can you see?

How many giraffes?

How many snakes?

How many monkeys?

Rearranging things

Are there the same number of mice in each set?

Are there the same number of bees in each set?

Are there the same number of beads in each set?

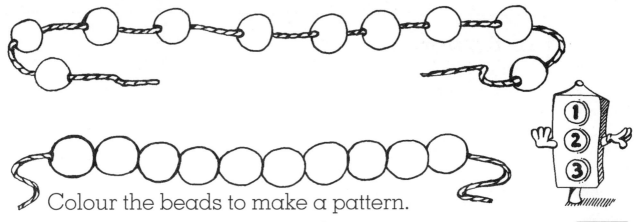

Colour the beads to make a pattern.

Making sets of things

Draw pictures to match the numbers.

4 cups

5 trees

6 hats

7 balls

8 sticks

9 bats

10 flowers

Making up to 10

Draw spots on the ladybirds.
Each ladybird must have 10 spots.

Colour the things which have exactly 8 spots.

Knowing the order of numbers

Join up the dots in order.

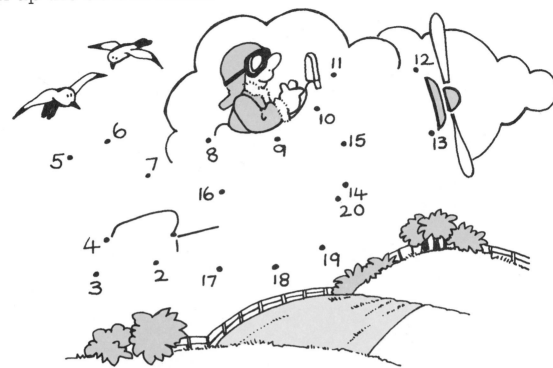

Follow the numbers 1 to 20 in order.
Trace your path through the wood.

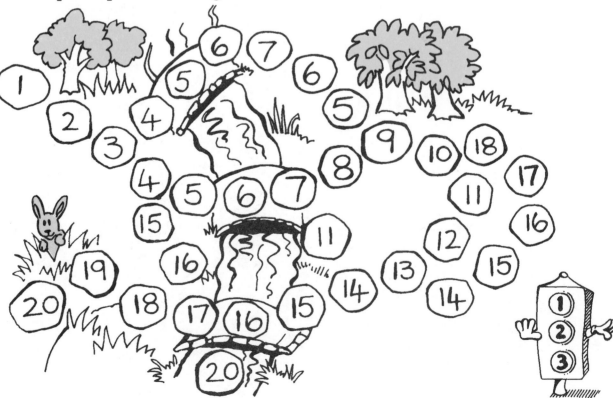

Writing numbers in order

Write in the missing numbers.

Using number words

Copy the number words.

one two three four five

six seven eight nine ten

Write a number word to go with each picture.

Making number patterns

Finish these number chains.

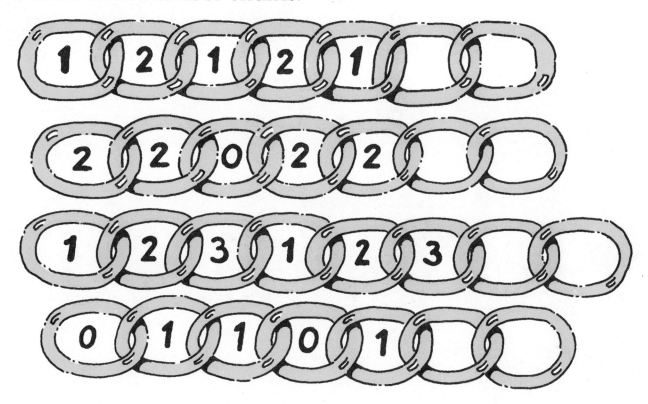

Make a different pattern of spots to go on each card.

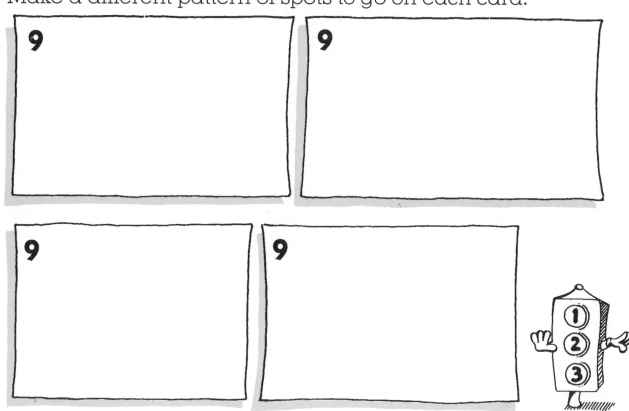

Counting

Say how many in each pot.

Reading

What do these numbers say?

Writing

Write how many.

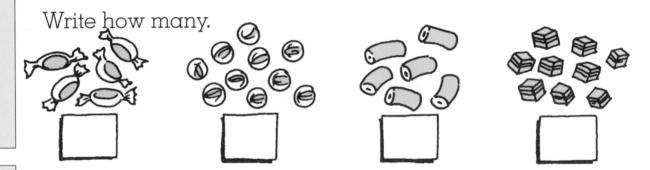

Ordering

Join these in order.

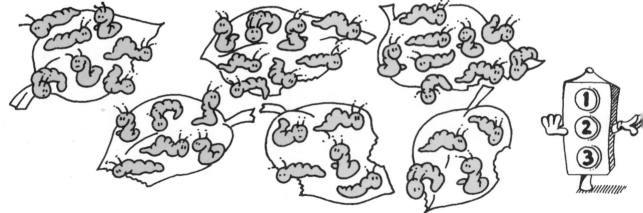

Counting, reading, writing and ordering

Write the number on each card.
Join the cards in order.

Now say the number on each card.

Adding sets together

Add the sets together, and write in the number.

birds

cats

dogs

Adding up in games

Add up the total of each of these sets of cards.

Add up the total of each set of dice.

Add up the total of each set of dominoes.

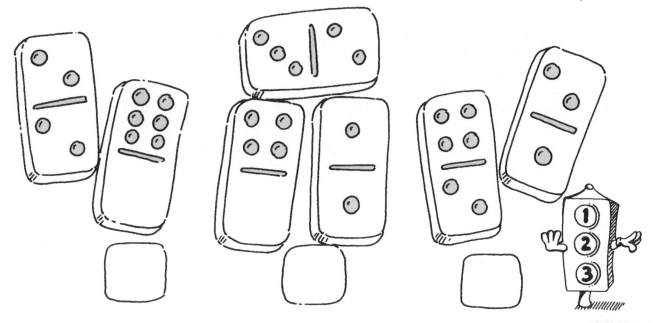

Using a number track

Join each total to the number track.

| 1 |
| 2 |
| 3 |
| 4 |
| 5 |
| 6 |
| 7 |
| 8 |
| 9 |
| 10 |

Taking away

Draw what is left behind every time.

Eat 3 of the apples.

Burst 5 of the balloons.

Pick 5 of the flowers.

Adding things

Draw the answers.

Subtracting things

Draw the answers.

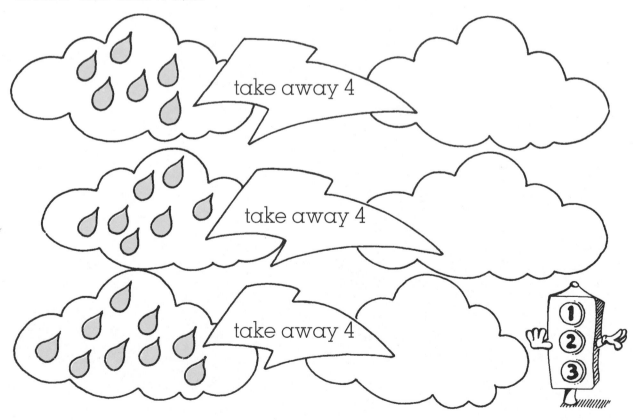

Adding and subtracting

This is Tommy Taker.
He takes 3 from everything he sees.

This is Annie Adder.
She adds 4 to everything she sees.

Draw what is left each time.

Making up addition sums

Write an addition sum under each picture.

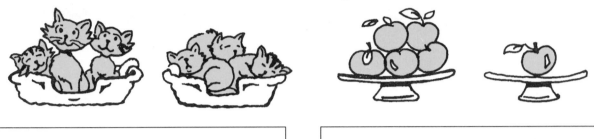

| | = | | | = |

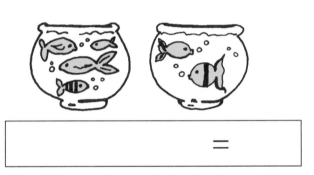

| | = | | | = |

Using addition sums

Draw a picture to go with each sum.

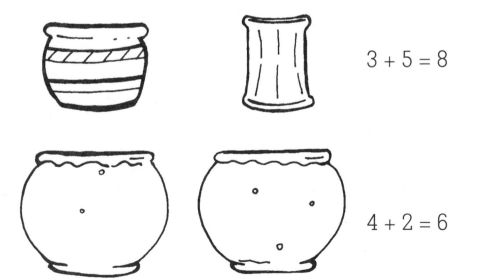

$3 + 5 = 8$

$4 + 2 = 6$

Using a number line

Join each cloud to a number on the number line.
Some clouds have more than one right answer.

the number between 3 and 5

the number after 5

the number 5

a number next to 1

the number before 2

the number seven

a number after 3

the number eight

the number before 5

the number ten

Order of things

Colour the third one red.
Colour the last one blue.

How many are there in each set?

Tick the set with the most.

Putting things in order

Draw a ball on the 3rd step up.

Draw a cat on the top step.

Draw a boy on the bottom step.

Draw a girl on the 4th step up.

Draw a hat on the 2nd step up.

Making number sequences

Write in the missing numbers.

Describing with measuring words

Draw long ears on
this rabbit.

Draw a short tail on
this dog.

Draw a tall tree in
this garden.

Draw wide stripes
on this tiger.

Comparing things

Tick the taller giraffe.

Colour the thinner girl.

Colour the wider river.

Tick the shorter plant.

Colour the longer scarf.

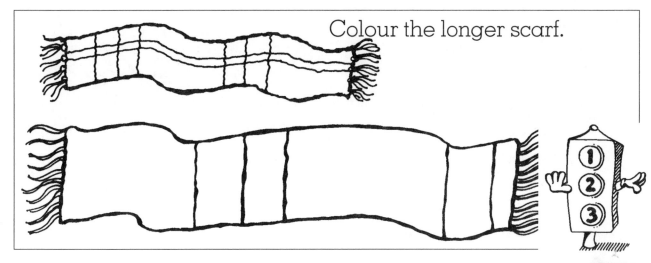

Comparing measures

Draw a longer snake.

Draw a shorter man.

Draw a bigger balloon.

Draw a taller ladder.

Draw a thinner mouse.

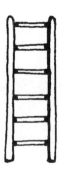

Ordering sizes

Colour the longest snake.
Colour the biggest elephant.
Draw a scarf on the smallest monkey.
Draw a fish in the widest open mouth.
Colour the bird in the tallest tree.

Finding opposites

Draw a line between the opposites.

in

hot

cold

slow

front

out

wet

back

fast

dry

Counting opposites

How many birds are on top of trees? ☐

How many birds are at the bottom of trees? ☐

How many people are inside cars? ☐

How many people are outside cars? ☐

How many monkeys are around the cars? ☐

How many monkeys are away from the cars? ☐

Using time words

Ring the answers.

Who is the youngest?

Who is late?

Who is early?

Who is the oldest?

Putting things in order

Each of these stories has got jumbled up.
Put numbers underneath to show the right order.

Talking about day and night

At night some animals wake up.
Draw a ring round each one in the picture.

What else is different about the two pictures?

Knowing the days of the week

Start with Sunday.
Join up the days of the week in order.

Monday

Tuesday

Wednesday

Saturday

Sunday

Friday

Thursday

Knowing about special days

Join up the words to the pictures.

Birthday

Christmas day

Bonfire day

Holidays

When is your birthday?

Looking at clocks

Clocks come in all shapes and sizes.
Join up pairs of clocks which tell the same time.
Colour the clock which is the odd one out.

The numbers are missing from this clock face.
Write them in.

Telling the time

Join up the clocks to the times.

1 o'clock

2 o'clock

3 o'clock

4 o'clock

5 o'clock

6 o'clock

7 o'clock

8 o'clock

9 o'clock

10 o'clock

11 o'clock

12 o'clock

Knowing words about position

How many pears are on the tree? ☐

Draw a ball in front of the tree.

What is peeping from behind the tree?

Colour the pears which have fallen off the tree.

How many birds are in the nest? ☐

Draw a cloud up in the sky.

_____

Colour the cat which is under the seat.

Using words about position

Colour all the mice which are inside something.

Colour all the bears which are under something.

Colour all the cats which are on top of something.

Describing with shape words

Draw curly hair on the clown.

Draw spikey leaves on the plant.

Draw some round balloons.

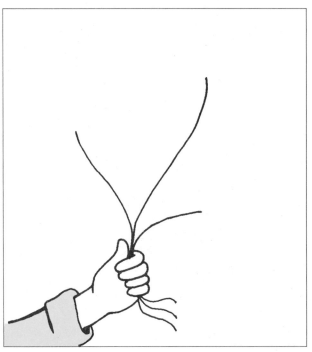

Draw some pointed teeth.

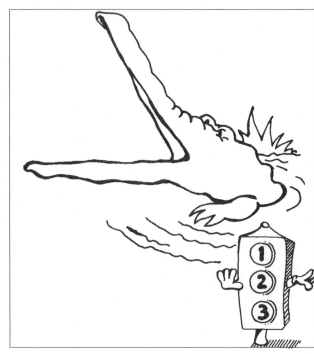

Sorting shapes

Choose a set of shapes which go together.
Colour your set red.

Choose a set of shapes which go together.
Draw a ring round your set.

How many of the fruits can you name?

Sorting flat shapes

Colour the shapes which are curved.

Colour the shapes which have three sides.

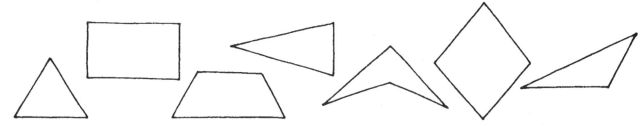

Make some of these shapes look like windows.

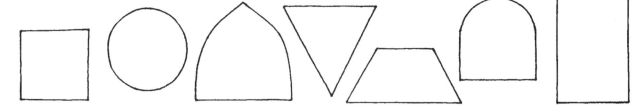

Sorting solid shapes

Colour the shapes which can roll.

Colour the shapes which have all flat faces.

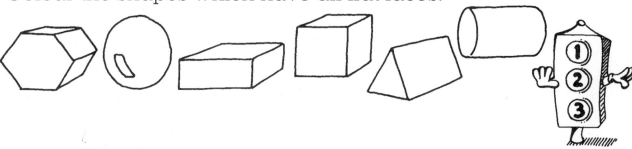

Sorting mixed shapes

Colour all the solid shapes.
Leave the flat shapes white.

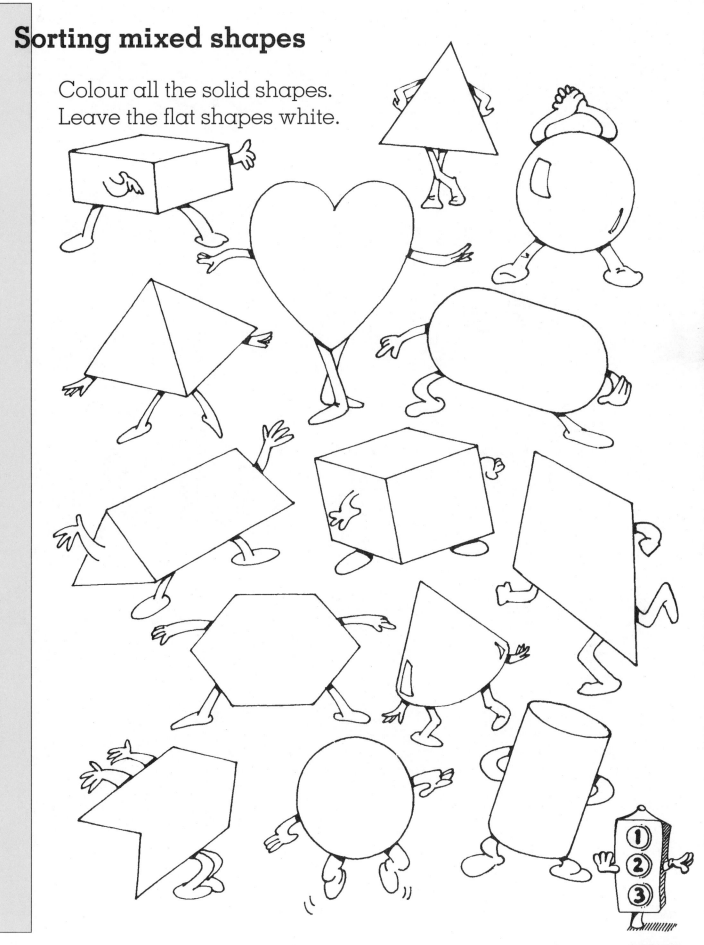

Finding shapes

I spy spiral shapes.
Colour them blue.

I spy shapes with holes in them.
Fill in the holes.

I spy circles.
Colour them green.

Matching shapes

Join pairs of pictures together.
One picture should be part of the other.

Shape outlines

Join each shape to its shadow.

Join each shape to its hole.

Shape patterns

Draw zig-zag patterns on these shapes.

Colour the odd one out.

Draw and colour patterns on these snakes.
Make each snake look different.

Reading information

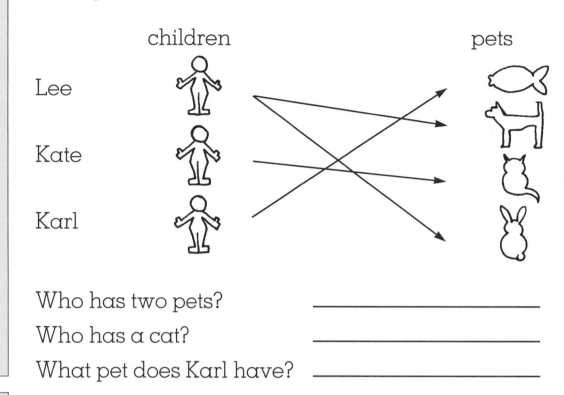

children   pets

Lee

Kate

Karl

Who has two pets?   _____

Who has a cat?   _____

What pet does Karl have?   _____

Interpreting information

Children   **Pets**

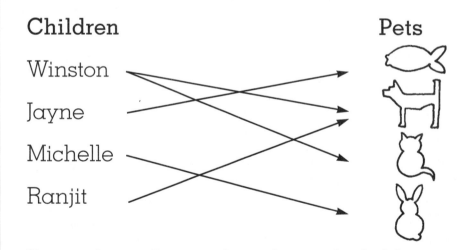

Winston

Jayne

Michelle

Ranjit

Draw the right pets beside each child.

Winston   Jayne   Michelle   Ranjit

Recording information

Here are some children and their pets.

Sarah   Michael   Amy   Ben

Fill in all the lines.

Children   Pets

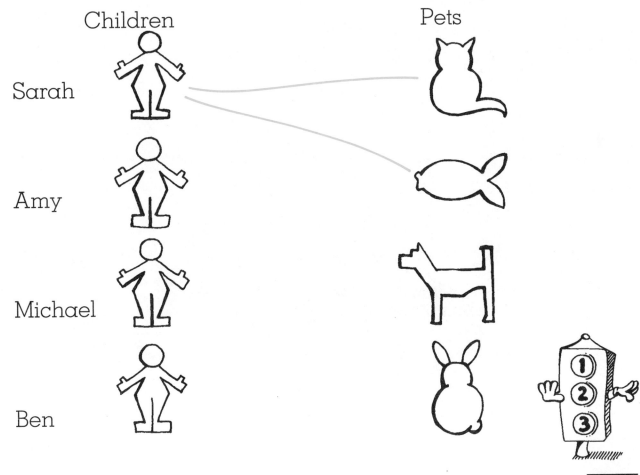

Sarah

Amy

Michael

Ben

Finding reasons for sorting

Draw a ring round the odd one out in each set.

Choose a set from these toys which go together.
Colour your set.

Looking for differences

Look at these two pictures very carefully.
Draw a ring round the things which are different.

How many differences did you find?

National Curriculum

This grid shows how each activity is related to the National Curriculum in maths; it will therefore give some idea of the educational purpose of each activity.

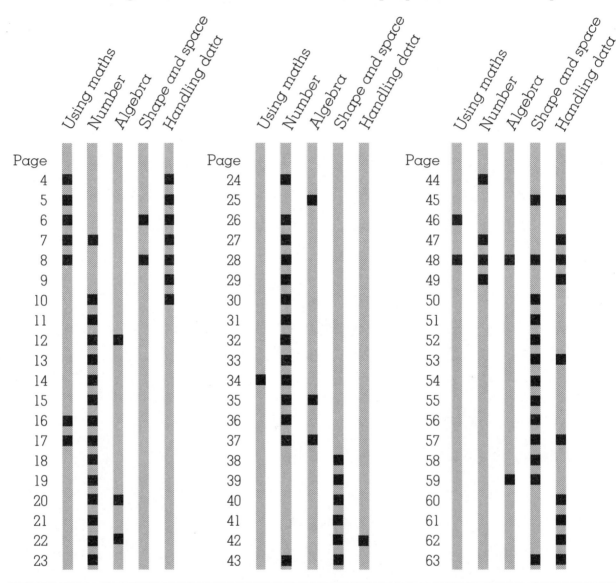

Oxford University Press, Walton Street, Oxford OX2 6DP

Oxford   New York
Athens Auckland Bangkok Bombay
Calcutta Cape Town Dar es Salaam Delhi
Florence Hong Kong Istanbul Karachi
Kuala Lumpur Madras Madrid Melbourne
Mexico City Nairobi Paris Singapore
Taipei Tokyo Toronto

and associated companies in
Berlin Ibadan

Oxford is a trade mark of Oxford University Press
© Peter Patilla 1992
First published 1992
Reprinted 1992, 1994 (twice), 1995

ISBN 0 19 838123 9

Designed by Plum Design, Southampton
Illustrations by Lynda Knott and Jason Smith
Cover illustration by Andy Cooke

Printed in Hong Kong